Jazz Classics

23 classic songs for keyboard

Published 1997

Music arranged & processed by Barnes Music Engraving Ltd East Sussex TN34 1HA
Cover Image David Redfern / Redferns Music Picture Library

© International Music Publications Ltd
Griffin House 161 Hammersmith Road London England W6 8BS

After You've Gone

Words and Music by Henry Creamer and Turner Layton

Suggested Registration: Accordian
Rhythm: Slow Swing   Jazz Club
Tempo: ♩ = 98

Af - ter you've gone __ and left me cry - ing,

af - ter you've gone __ there's no de - ny - ing you'll feel blue, __

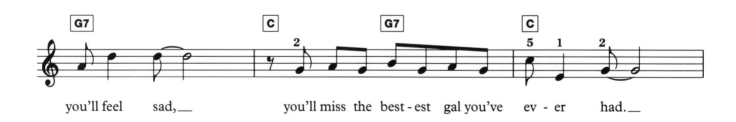

you'll feel sad, __ you'll miss the best - est gal you've ev - er had. __

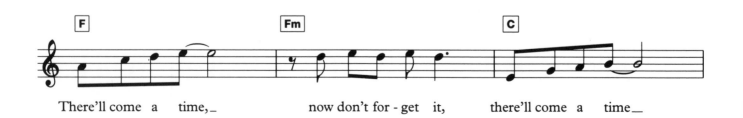

There'll come a time, __ now don't for - get it, there'll come a time __

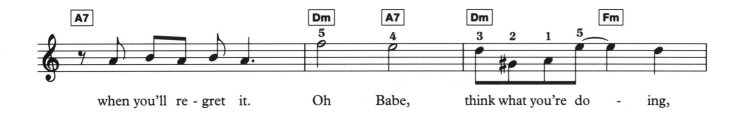

when you'll re - gret it. Oh Babe, think what you're do - ing,

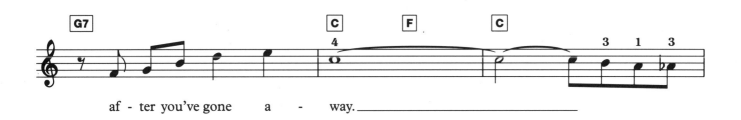

you know my love for you will drive me to ru - in af - ter you've gone,

af - ter you've gone a - way. _____

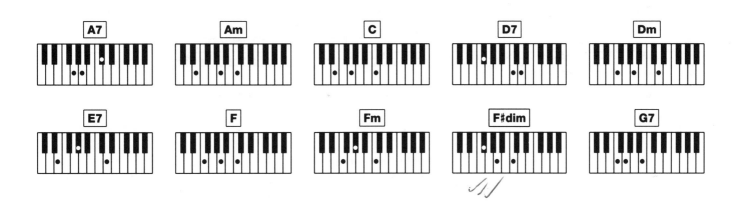

Come Rain Or Come Shine

Words by Johnny Mercer / Music by Harold Arlen

Suggested Registration: Brass
Rhythm: Swing
Tempo: ♩ = 120

I'm gon-na love you like no - bo-dy's loved you, come rain or come shine._____

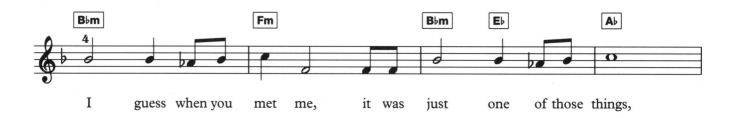

High as a moun-tain and deep as a riv-er, come rain or come shine._____

I guess when you met me, it was just one of those things,

but don't ev - er bet me 'cause I'm gon-na be true if you let me.

You're gon-na love me like no - bo-dy's loved me, come rain or come shine._____

Hap - py to - ge - ther, un - hap - py to - ge - ther, and won't it be fine._____

Days may be cloud-y or sun - ny, we're in or we're out of the mon - ey, but

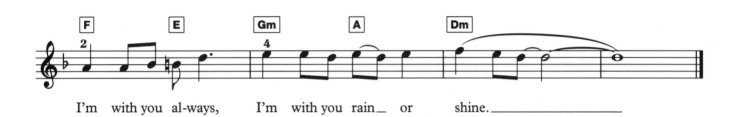

I'm with you al-ways, I'm with you rain__ or shine._____

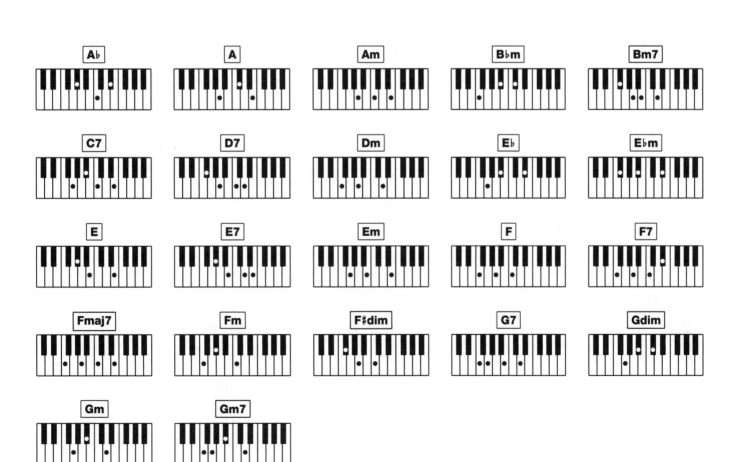

Do Nothin' Till You Hear From Me

Words and Music by Bob Russell and Duke Ellington

Suggested Registration: Brass
Rhythm: Swing
Tempo: ♩ = 100

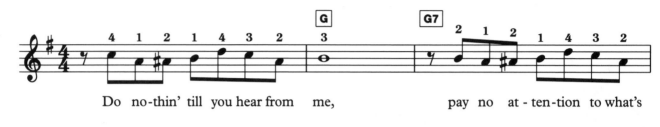

Do no-thin' till you hear from me, pay no at-ten-tion to what's

said. Why peo-ple tear the seam of a-ny-one's dream____

__ is o-ver my head.__ Do no-thin' till you hear from me,

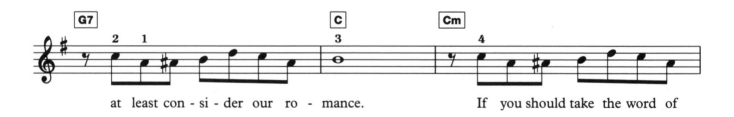

at least con-si-der our ro-mance. If you should take the word of

oth-ers you've heard,_____ I have-n't a chance.__

True, I've been seen with some-one new,_ but does that mean

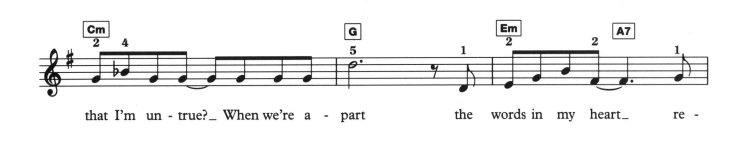

that I'm un-true?_ When we're a - part   the words in my heart_   re -

-veal how I feel__ a - bout you.____ Some kiss may cloud my mem - o - ry,

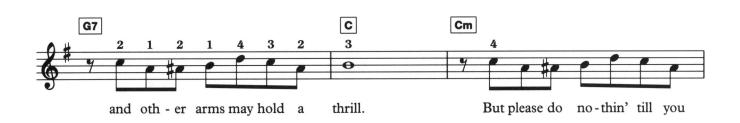

and oth - er arms may hold a   thrill.   But please do no - thin' till you

hear it from me,_____ and you ne - ver will.___

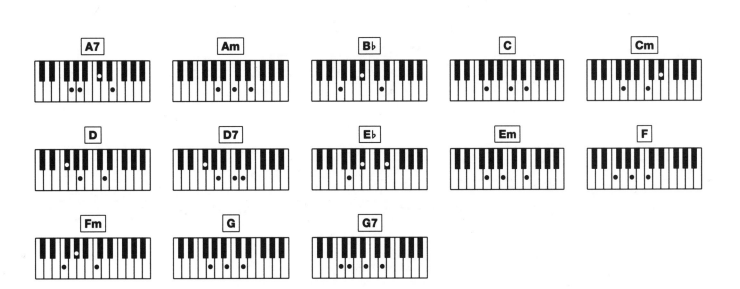

Harlem Nocturne

Music by Earle Hagen

Suggested Registration: Saxophone
Rhythm: Slow Rock
Tempo: ♩ = 80

HERE'S THAT RAINY DAY

Words by Johnny Burke / Music by James Van Heusen

Suggested Registration: Vibraphone
Rhythm: Bossa Nova
Tempo: ♩ = 108

May - be   I   should have   saved those   left - o - ver

dreams;   Fun - ny,   but   here's that   rain - y   day._____

—   Here's   that   rain - y   day   they

told   me   a - bout,   and   I   laughed   at   the thought   that   it

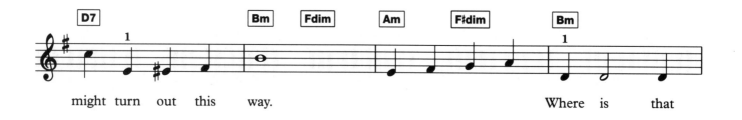

might turn   out   this   way.   Where   is   that

worn out wish that I threw a - side, af - ter it

brought my lov - er near? Fun - ny how

love be - comes a cold rain - y day. Fun - ny that

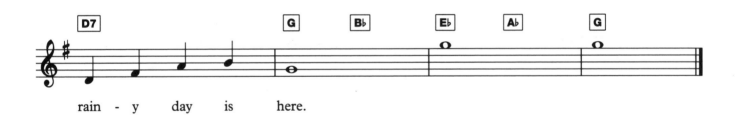

rain - y day is here.

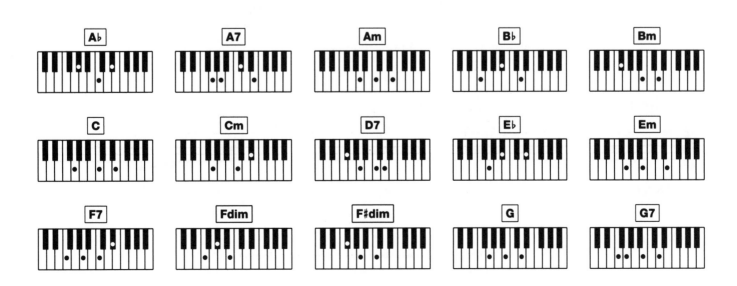

Honeysuckle Rose

Words by Andy Razaf / Music by Fats Waller

Suggested Registration: Jazz Guitar
Rhythm: Swing
Tempo: ♩ = 116

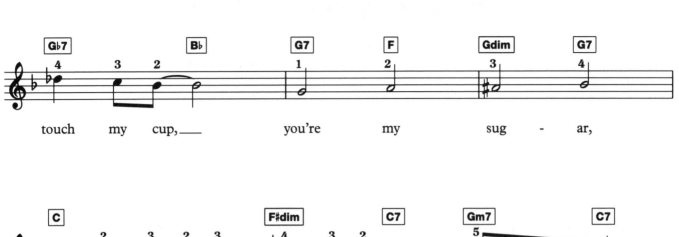

touch my cup,___ you're my sug - ar,

it's sweet when you stir it up.___ When I'm tak - in' sips

from your tas - ty lips, seems the hon - ey fair - ly drips, you're con - fec - tion,

good - ness knows,___ Hon - ey - suck - le Rose.

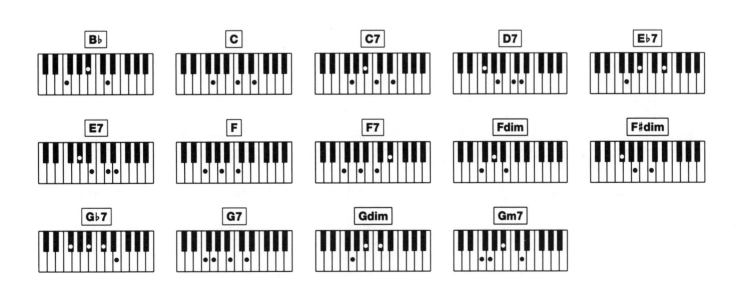

It Don't Mean A Thing
(If It Ain't Got That Swing)

Words by Irving Mills / Music by Duke Ellington

Suggested Registration: Jazz Organ
Rhythm: Swing
Tempo: ♩ = 170

It don't mean a thing if it ain't got that swing,

_ doo wah,_ doo wah, doo wah, doo wah, doo wah,_

_ doo wah, doo wah, doo wah. It don't mean a thing, all you

got to do is sing, doo wah, doo wah, doo wah, doo wah, doo wah,

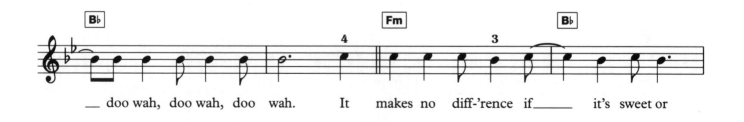

_ doo wah, doo wah, doo wah. It makes no diff'rence if____ it's sweet or

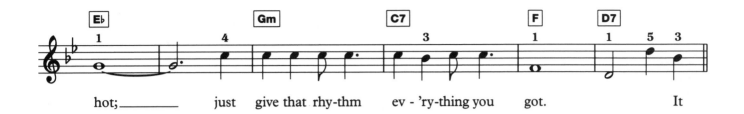

hot;_____ just give that rhy-thm ev - 'ry-thing you got. It

don't mean a thing if it ain't got that swing,

doo wah, doo wah, doo wah, doo wah, doo wah,_ doo wah, doo wah, doo wah.

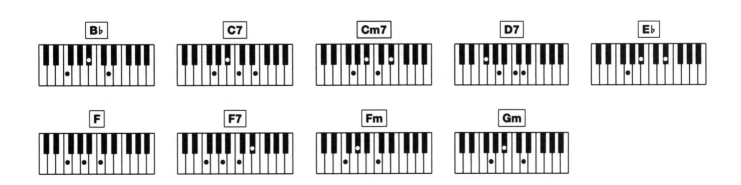

It's All Right With Me

Words and Music by Cole Porter

Suggested Registration: Vibraphone or Jazz Guitar
Rhythm: Swing
Tempo: ♩ = 152

Jeepers Creepers

Words by Johnny Mercer / Music by Harry Warren

Suggested Registration: Trumpet
Rhythm: Swing
Tempo: ♩ = 160

Jeep - ers Creep - ers! Where'd ya get those

peep - ers? Jeep - ers Creep - ers! Where'd ya get those

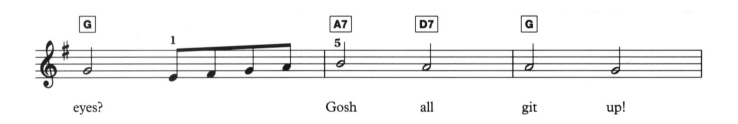

eyes? Gosh all git up!

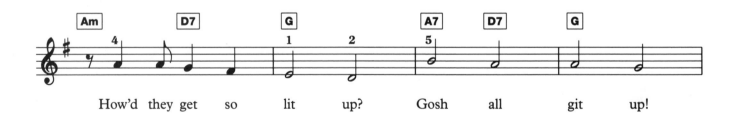

How'd they get so lit up? Gosh all git up!

How'd they get that size? Gol - ly gee!

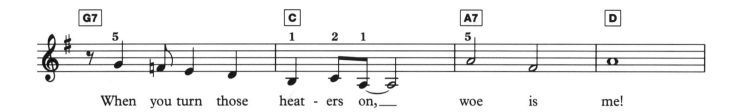

When you turn those heat - ers on,___ woe is me!

Got to put my cheat - ers on.___ Jeep - ers Creep - ers!

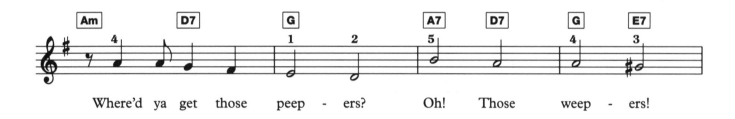

Where'd ya get those peep - ers? Oh! Those weep - ers!

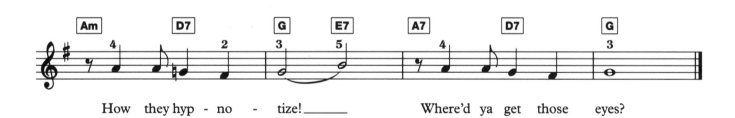

How they hyp - no - tize!_____ Where'd ya get those eyes?

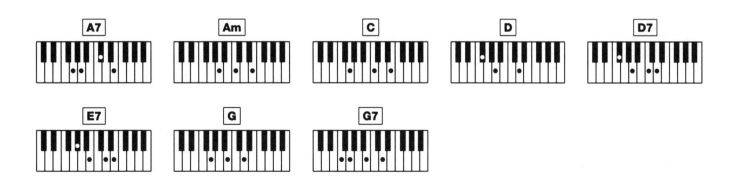

LAURA

Words by Johnny Mercer / Music by David Raksin

Suggested Registration: Strings
Rhythm: Bossa Nova
Tempo: ♩ = 96

Lau - ra_____ is the face in the mist - y light,_____

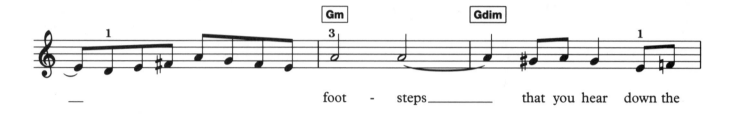

— foot - steps_____ that you hear down the

hall. The laugh_____

— that floats on a sum - mer night,_____ that you can

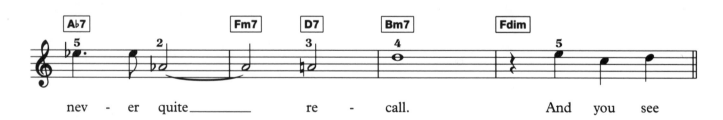

nev - er quite_____ re - call. And you see

Lau - ra_____ on the train that is pass - ing through.____

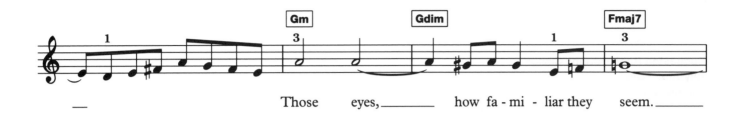

Those eyes,_____ how fa - mi - liar they seem._____

She gave_____ your ve - ry first kiss to you._____

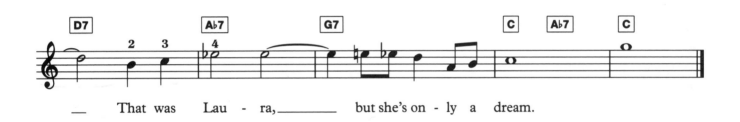

That was Lau - ra,_____ but she's on - ly a dream.

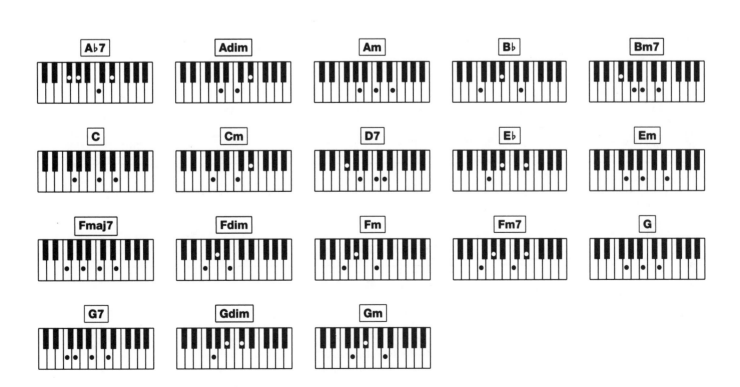

Love For Sale

Words and Music by Cole Porter

Suggested Registration: Clarinet
Rhythm: Swing
Tempo: ♩ = 84

Misty

Words Johnny Burke / Music by Erroll Garner

Suggested Registration: Piano
Rhythm: Bossa Nova
Tempo: ♩ = 84

Look at me, I'm as help-less as a kit-ten up a tree and I feel like I'm cling-ing to a cloud, I can't un-der-stand, I get mist - y just hold-ing your hand. Walk my way and a thou-sand vi-o-lins be-gin to play, or it might be the sound of your hel-lo, that mu-sic I hear, I get mist - y the mo-ment you're near. You can say that you're lead-ing me on,_____ but it's just what I

want you to do,_____ don't you no - tice how hope-less - ly I'm lost,_____

_ that's why I'm fol - low-ing you. On my own, would I

wan-der through this won-der-land a - lone, nev-er know-ing my right foot from my left, my

hat from my glove, I'm too mist - y and too much in love.

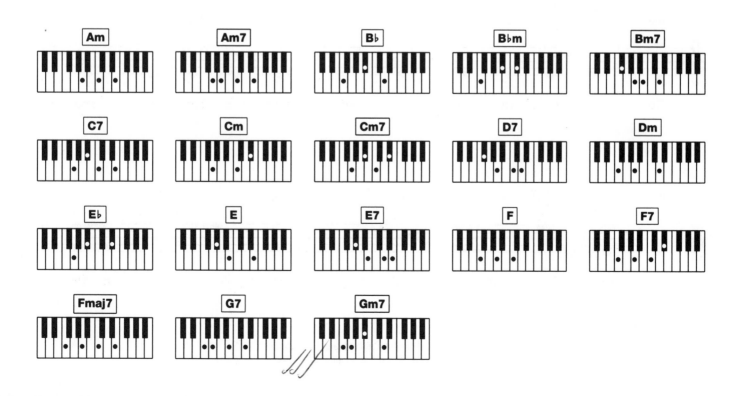

Moonlight In Vermont

Words by John Blackburn / Music by Karl Suessdorf

Suggested Registration: Vibraphone
Rhythm: Slow Swing
Tempo: ♩ = 80

Pen - nies in a stream, fall - ing leaves, a syc - a-more,

moon-light in Ver - mont. I - cy fin - ger - waves,

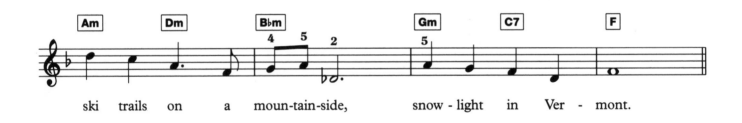

ski trails on a moun-tain-side, snow - light in Ver - mont.

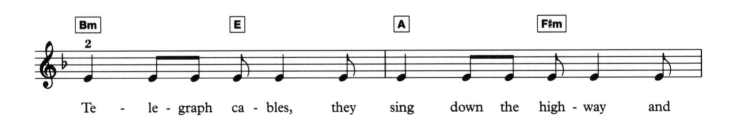

Te - le - graph ca - bles, they sing down the high - way and

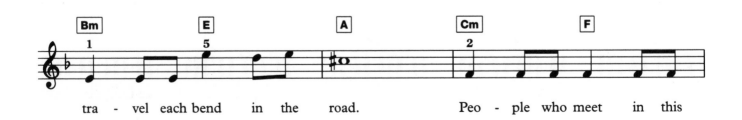

tra - vel each bend in the road. Peo - ple who meet in this

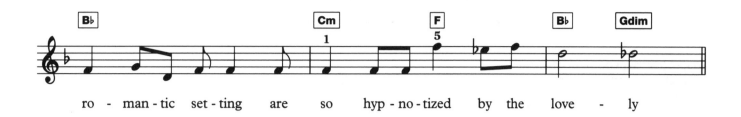

ro - man -tic set -ting are so hyp -no -tized by the love - ly

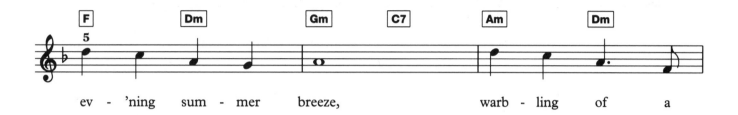

ev - 'ning sum - mer breeze, warb - ling of a

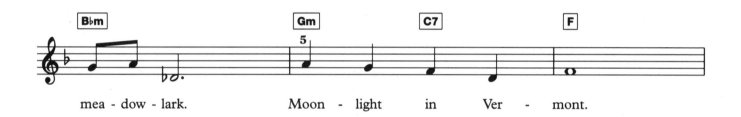

mea -dow -lark. Moon - light in Ver - mont.

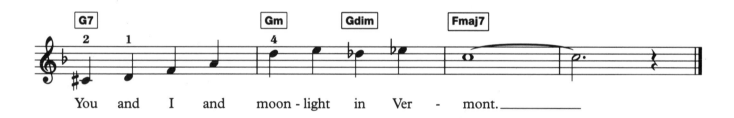

You and I and moon -light in Ver - mont._____

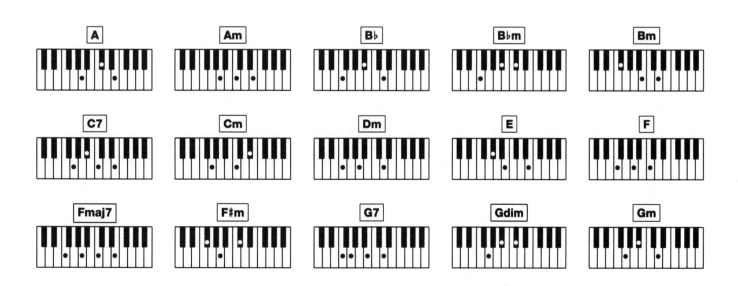

More Than You Know

Words by Edward Eliscu and Billy Rose / Music by Vincent Youmans

Suggested Registration: Trombone
Rhythm: Jazz Swing
Tempo: ♩ = 92

no-thing I can do a - bout it. Lov-ing may-be

all you can give, but hon - ey, I can't live with - out it. (hum___

___) Oh, how I'd cry, oh, how I'd cry, if you got tired and said 'good -

- bye', more than I'd show, more than you'd ev - er know.

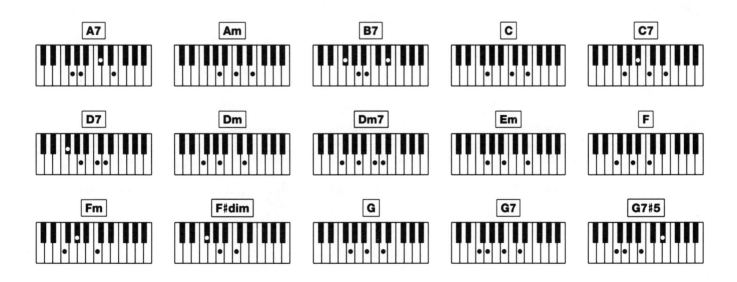

Old Devil Moon

Words by E Y Harburg / Music by Burton Lane

Suggested Registration: Trombone
Rhythm: Swing
Tempo: ♩ = 144

On Green Dolphin Street

Words by Ned Washington / Music by Bronislau Kaper

Suggested Registration: Jazz Organ
Rhythm: Swing
Tempo: ♩ = 116

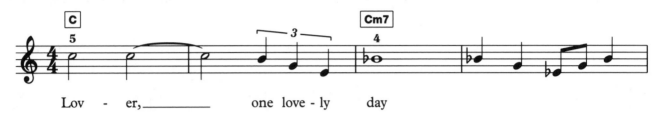

Lov - er,_____ one love - ly day

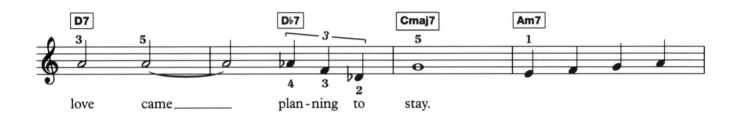

love came_____ plan - ning to stay.

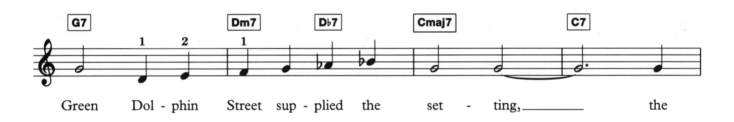

Green Dol - phin Street sup - plied the set - ting,_____ the

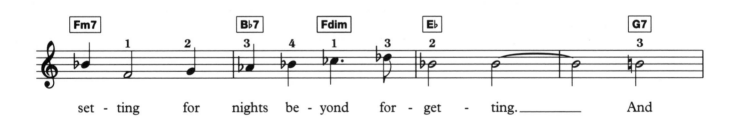

set - ting for nights be - yond for - get - ting._____ And

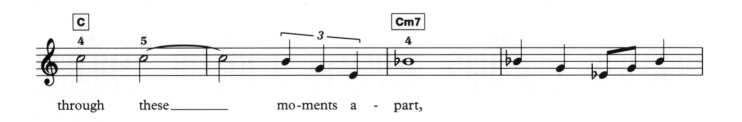

through these_____ mo - ments a - part,

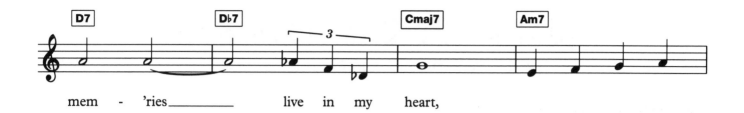

mem - 'ries_____ live in my heart,

when I re - call the love I found on, I could kiss the

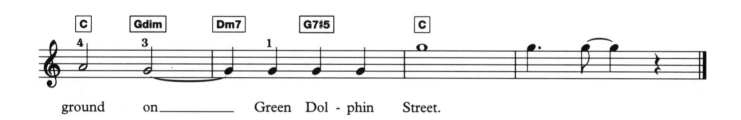

ground on_____ Green Dol - phin Street.

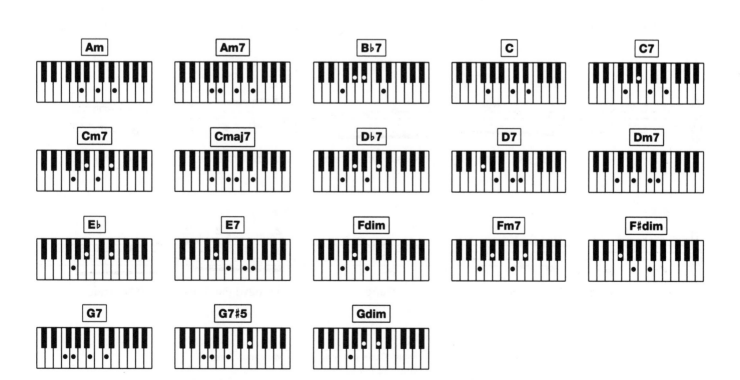

One Note Samba
(Samba De Una Nota So)

Words by Newton Mendonca / Music by Antonio Carlos Jobim

Suggested Registration: Jazz Guitar or Flute
Rhythm: Bossa Nova
Tempo: ♩ = 138

This is just a lit-tle sam-ba built up-on a sin-gle note.

Oth-er notes are bound to fol-low, but the root is still that note.

Now the new one is the con-se-quence of the one we've just been

through, as I'm bound to be the un-a-void-a-ble con-se-quence of you.

There's so ma-ny peo-ple who can talk and talk and talk and just say

no-thing, or near-ly no-thing. I have used up all the scale I

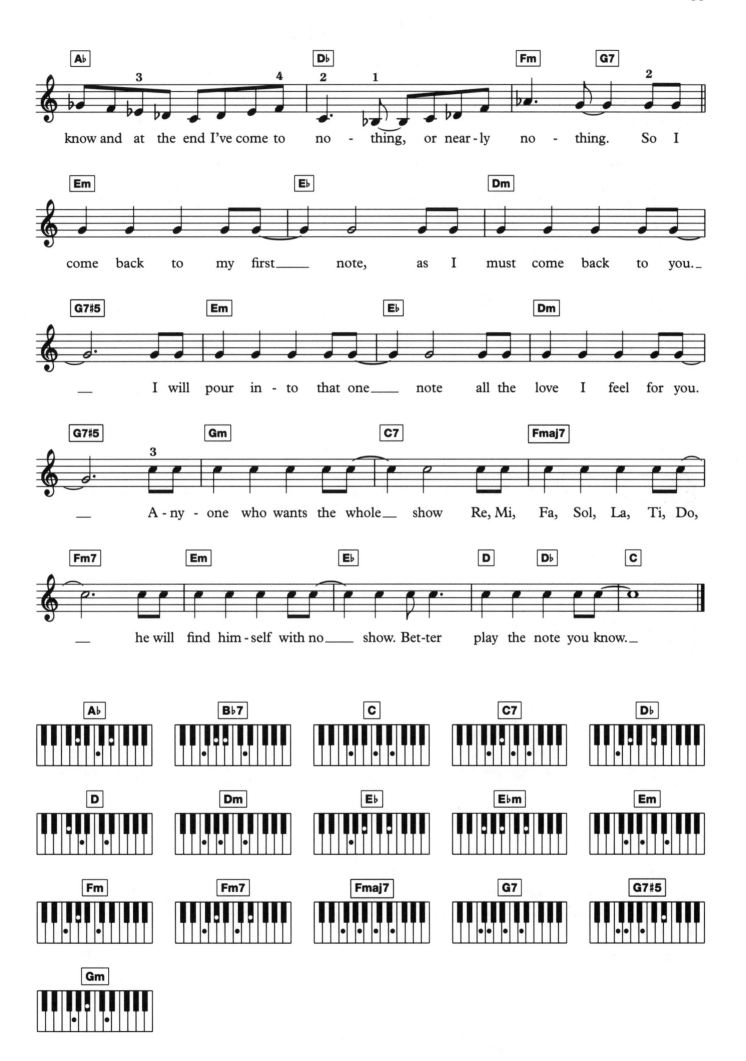

SATIN DOLL

Words and Music by Billy Strayhorn, Duke Ellington and Johnny Mercer

Suggested Registration: Vibraphone
Rhythm: Swing
Tempo: ♩ = 104

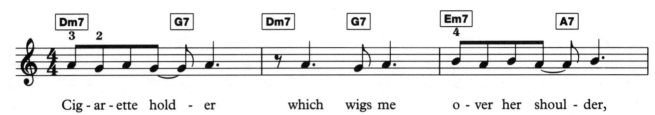

Cig-ar-ette hold - er which wigs me o - ver her shoul - der,

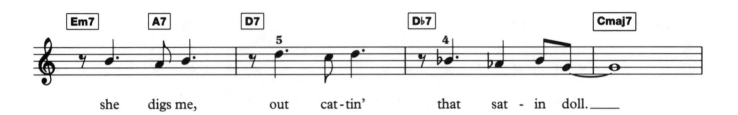

she digs me, out cat-tin' that sat - in doll.____

Ba - by shall we____ go out skip-in',

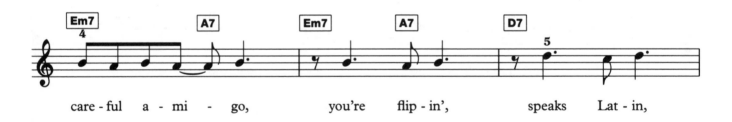

care - ful a - mi - go, you're flip - in', speaks Lat - in,

that sat - in doll.____ She's no - bo-dy's fool, so I'm

play - ing it cool as can be,_____ I'll

give it a whirl,_ but I ain't for no girl__ catch-ing me.___

Switch - E - Roo - ney Te - le-phone num - bers, well you know,

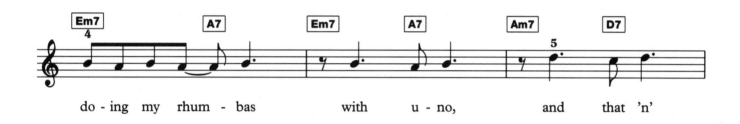

do - ing my rhum - bas with u - no, and that 'n'

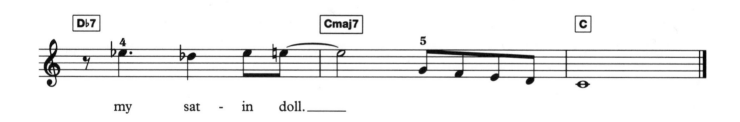

my sat - in doll.___

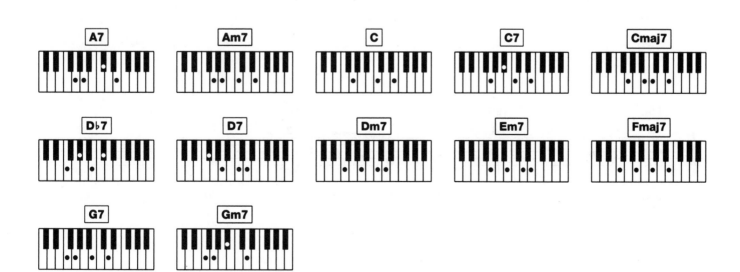

The Shadow Of Your Smile

Words by Paul Francis Webster / Music by Johnny Mandel

Suggested Registration: Electric Piano
Rhythm: Beguine
Tempo: ♩ = 96

The sha-dow of your smile when you are

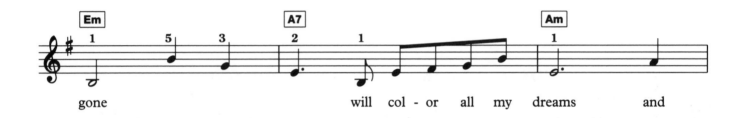

gone will col - or all my dreams and

light the dawn._____ Look in - to my eyes, my love, and

see_____ all the love - ly things you are to

me. Our wist-ful lit - tle star was far too

high,   a tear-drop kissed your   lips   and

so   did   I._____   Now when I re - mem - ber Spring,___

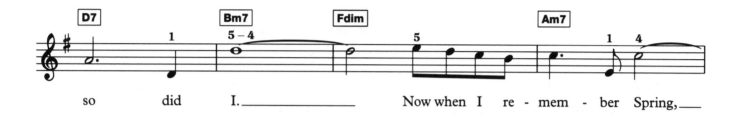

— all the joy that love   can bring,_____   I will be re - mem - ber-ing___

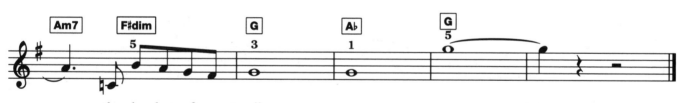

—   the sha-dow of your smile.

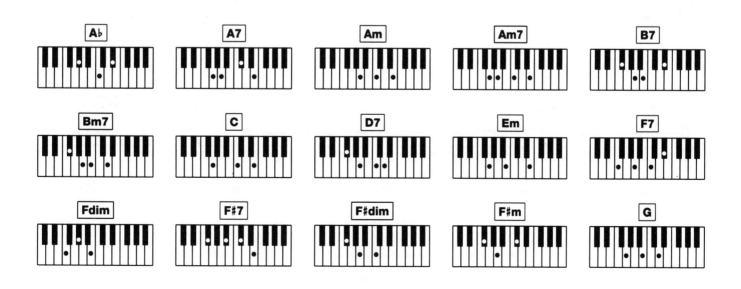

Skylark

Words by Johnny Mercer / Music by Hoagy Carmichael

Suggested Registration: Jazz Organ
Rhythm: Swing
Tempo: ♩ = 100

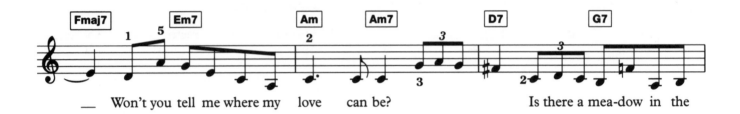

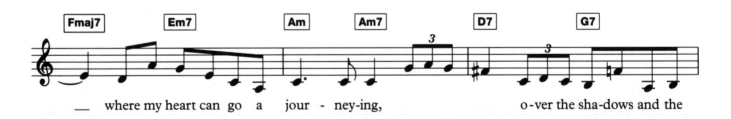

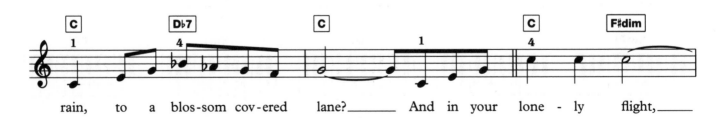

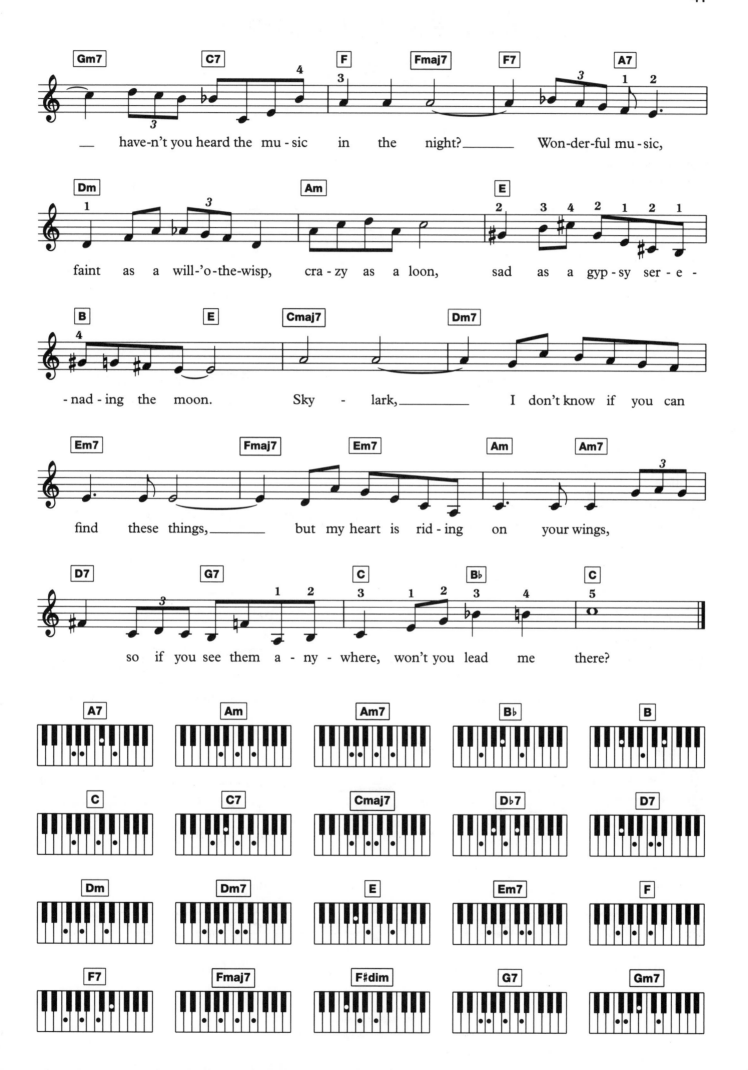

Spring Can Really Hang You Up The Most

Words by Frances Landesman / Music by Tommy Wolf

Suggested Registration: Piano
Rhythm: Slow Swing
Tempo: ♩ = 96

Spring this year has got me feel - ing like a horse that nev - er left the

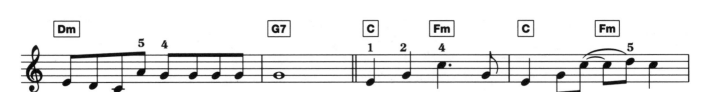

post; I lie in my room___ star - ing up at the ceil - ing,

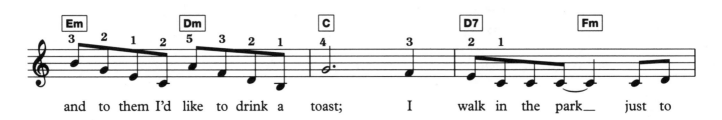

spring can real-ly hang you up the most. Morn-ing's kiss wakes trees and flow - ers,

and to them I'd like to drink a toast; I walk in the park___ just to

kill lone - ly hours,____ spring can real - ly hang you up the most.

All af - ter-noon those birds twit - ter twit, I know the tune, "This is

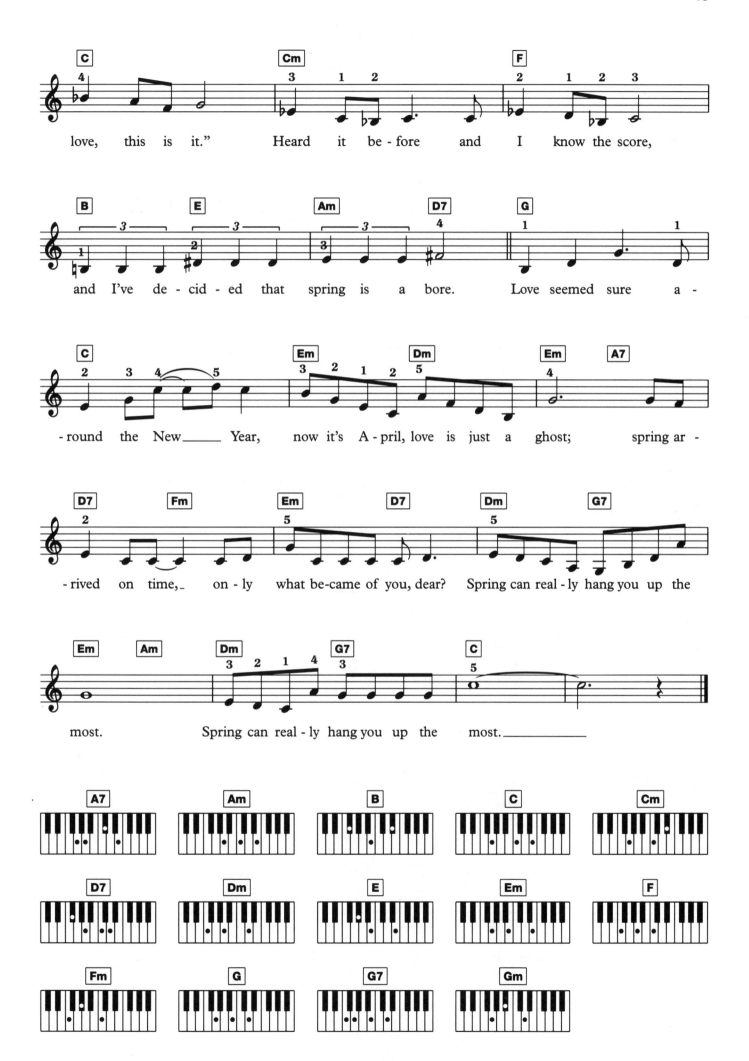

Star Dust

Words by Mitchell Parish / Music by Hoagy Carmichael

Suggested Registration: Strings
Rhythm: Slow Swing
Tempo: ♩ = 80

Some - times I won - der why I spend the lone - ly

night dream - ing of a song, the mel - o - dy

haunts my rev - er - ie, and I am once a - gain with you, when our

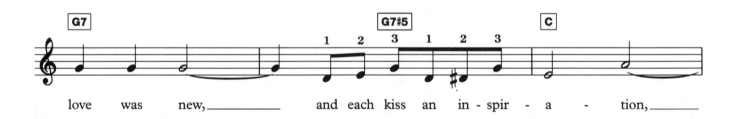

love was new,_____ and each kiss an in - spir - a - tion,_____

_ but that was long a - go, now my con - so - la - tion is

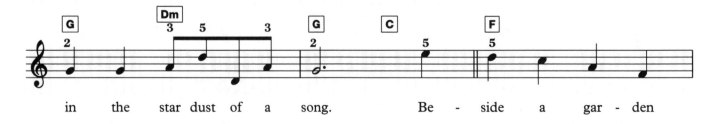

in the star dust of a song. Be - side a gar - den

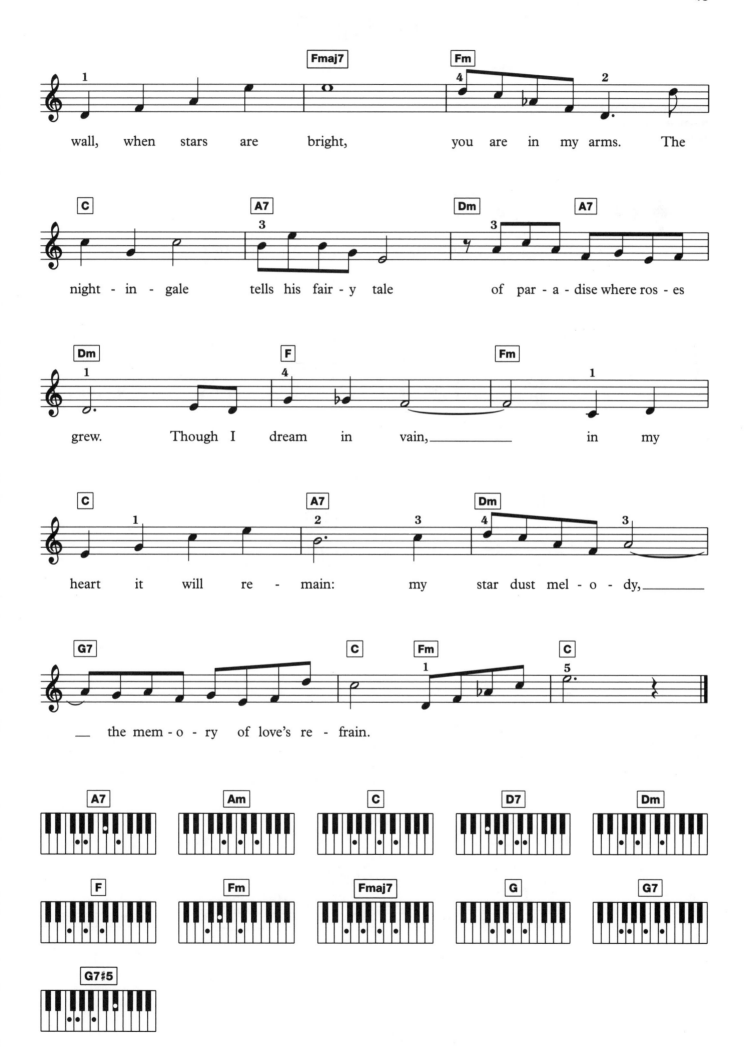

Take The "A" Train

Words and Music by Billy Strayhorn and The Delta Rhythm Boys

Suggested Registration: Brass
Rhythm: Swing
Tempo: ♩ = 150

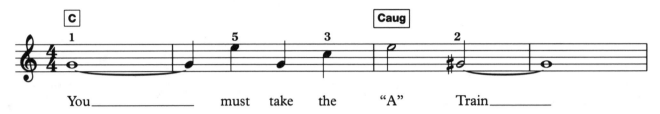

You_____ must take the "A" Train_____

to go to Sug-ar Hill way up in Har - lem._____

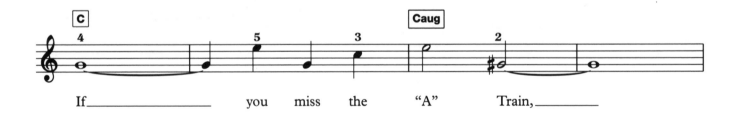

If_____ you miss the "A" Train,_____

you'll find you've missed the quick-est way to Har - lem.

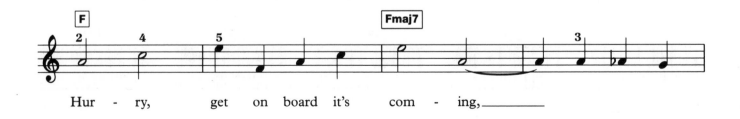

Hur - ry, get on board it's com - ing,_____

lis - ten   to those rails a - thrum - ming,_____   on

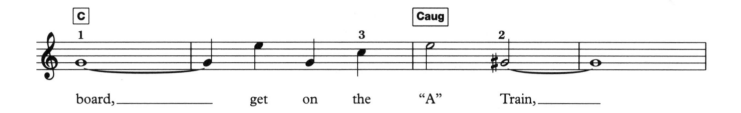

board,_____   get   on   the   "A"   Train,_____

soon   you will be on Sug-ar Hill in   Har - lem.

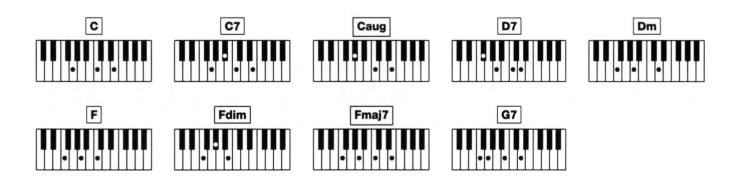

The Easy Keyboard Library Series

Big Band Hits
Order Ref: 19098

Popular Classics
Order Ref: 4180A

Blues
Order Ref: 3477A

Pub Singalong Collection
Order Ref: 3954A

Celebration Songs
Order Ref: 3478A

Rock 'n' Roll Classics
Order Ref: 2224A

Christmas Carols
Order Ref: 4616A

Traditional Scottish Favourites
Order Ref: 4231A

Christmas Songs
Order Ref: 19198

Showtunes - Volume 1
Order Ref: 19103

Classic Hits - Volume 1
Order Ref: 19099

Showtunes - Volume 2
Order Ref: 3328A

Classic Hits - Volume 2
Order Ref: 19100

Soft Rock Collection
Order Ref: 4617A

Country Songs
Order Ref: 19101

Soul Classics
Order Ref: 19201

Traditional English Favourites
Order Ref: 4229A

Summer Collection
Order Ref: 3489A

Favourite Hymns
Order Ref: 4179A

TV Themes
Order Ref: 19196

Film Classics
Order Ref: 19197

The Twenties
Order Ref: 2969A

Great Songwriters
Order Ref: 2225A

The Thirties
Order Ref: 2970A

Instrumental Classics
Order Ref: 2338A

The Forties
Order Ref: 2971A

Traditional Irish Favourites
Order Ref: 4230A

The Fifties
Order Ref: 2972A

Love Songs - Volume 1
Order Ref: 19102

The Sixties
Order Ref: 2973A

Love Songs - Volume 2
Order Ref: 19199

The Seventies
Order Ref: 2974A

Music Hall
Order Ref: 3329A

The Eighties
Order Ref: 2975A

Motown Classics
Order Ref: 2337A

The Nineties
Order Ref: 2976A

Number One Hits
Order Ref: 19200

Wartime Collection
Order Ref: 3955A

Wedding Collection
Order Ref: 3688A

Exclusive distributors:

International Music Publications Limited
Griffin House 161 Hammersmith Road, London W6 8BS
International Music Publications Limited
25 Rue D'Hauteville, 75010 Paris, France
International Music Publications GmbH Germany
Marstallstrasse 8, D-80539 München, Germany
Nuova Carisch S.R.L.
Via M.F. Quintiliano 40, 20138 Milano, Italy
Danmusik
Vognmagergade 7, DK-1120 Copenhagen K, Denmark

THE EASY KEYBOARD LIBRARY